THE BRITISH TV SITCOM QUIZ BOOK

THE BRITISH TV SITCOM QUIZ BOOK

Compiled by Chris Cowlin

Forewords by Brian Murphy and Nicholas Parsons OBE

APEX PUBLISHING LTD

First published in hardback in 2009 by

Apex Publishing Ltd

PO Box 7086, Clacton on Sea, Essex, CO15 5WN, England

www.apexpublishing.co.uk

British Library Cataloguing-in-Publication Data
A catalogue record for this book
is available from the British Library

ISBN: 1-906358-20-6   978-1-906358-20-4

Typeset in 10.5pt Chianti Bdlt Win95BT

Cover Design: Siobhan Smith

Printed and bound in Great Britain by
the MPG Books Group, Bodmin and King's Lynn

Dedication:
This book is dedicated to my wife Julia, my little boy Harry and my late baby daughter Sophie.

FOREWORD

I was fortunate enough to have appeared in what is now often regarded as the Golden Age of television sit-coms during the 70s and 80s.

In Man about the House and George and Mildred regular viewing figures were over 20 million for each episode. Those programmes were never out of the top five - proving how television viewers enjoyed laughing at good family entertainment.

They were happy times and Thames TV was responsible for offering the nation some of the very best in light entertainment. For me there was also the pleasure of working with the brilliantly talented Yootha Joyce, Richard O'Sullivan, Paula Wilcox and Sally Thomsett, we had many laughs on and off the set.

This book will bring back happy memories of those halcyon days and give the reader much fun in answering the questions.

Best wishes
Brian Murphy

FOREWORD

The British have always produced the best and most entertaining situation comedies. Unfortunately as production costs have increased and reality shows have become very popular, we are creating fewer memorable shows in this genre.

The best British comedies have always been based on character, as opposed to American sitcoms which are usually based on types, individuals who are easily recognised by the vast American audience to which they must appeal and the comedy usually arises from the clever dialogue the performers deliver.

In this country we have such a large diverse cross-section of distinctive and unusual individuals who in their own way are very British that our skilled comedy writers build wonderful situations around such characters. We recognise them, though they are slightly larger than life, and when the roles are performed by the great comedy actors this country produces you have wonderful situation comedy.

Take the example of that classic show DAD'S ARMY. A group of very British characters put in an unusual situation by clever writing, then superbly performed by skilled actors and you have a timeless comedy.

When you recall the great British sit-coms there are a number which immediately spring to mind, and the proof of their success and popularity is that they are regularly repeated on our television screens. They are nearly all based around a wonderful British character superbly performed. PORRIDGE with the incomparable Ronnie Barker as the wicked, wily and *conniving Fletcher. Also his equally creative performance in OPEN ALL HOURS, which also featured that other great comedy performer David Jason. His brilliant creation in ONLY FOOLS AND HORSES guarantees its constant repeats.*

It would take too long in a foreward to list all the great British situation comedies that have been created over the years and name the stars that helped to make these shows famous. Anyway most of them will be listed in this book. I will finish by mentioning a more recent comedy which has achieved great success and proves how creative we can be in this field of entertainment THE VICAR OF DIBLEY. The show proves all the points I have been trying to make. A simple but delightful setting, a cast of wonderful British characters, all a little larger than real life, but whom we recognise as typically British, played by first-class comedy performers, and the whole show revolving around a superb creation of the writers an attractive female vicar played with style and comic panache by the engaging and highly talented Dawn French.

In closing, Britain has always produced the best situation comedies. Most of these are based on characters we immediately recognise and with whom we can identify. These characters become much loved and fondly remembered, so a quiz book based on them and the situations in which they have been involved, must be a winner and popular with all television addicts.

Enjoy the book!

Best wishes
Nicholas Parsons OBE

INTRODUCTION

I would first of all like to thank Brian Murphy and Nicholas Parsons OBE for writing the forewords to this book. I have a lot of time for Brian and Nicholas, they are two great people and great servants to British Television. Brian still makes me laugh when I watch repeats of *George and Mildred* and *Man About The House.*

I would also like to thank all the newspapers, magazines and famous names who have backed this book and provided a few comments (these can be found at the back of the book).

I have compiled over 30 books and I must say this has been my favourite! The book has been an absolute joy to write, re-living the golden age and modern era of British comedy – you cannot put a price on it. This book has something for everyone, young or old, I have made sure it has questions about the most popular sitcoms and covers sitcoms back in the 60s, 70s, 80s, as well as the more recent sitcoms in the 1990s and today.

In closing, I would like to thank all my friends and family, especially my wife Julia, for encouraging me to complete this book.

Best wishes
Chris Cowlin

www.apexpublishing.co.uk

ONLY FOOLS AND HORSES

1. What colour was the Trotters' three-wheeled van?

2. In which part of London did the Trotters live?

3. How many series were there of this sitcom – 7, 8 or 9?

4. In which year was this sitcom first broadcast on the BBC – 1980, 1981 or 1982?

5. Which character called Rodney 'Dave'?

6. Can you name the actor who played Granddad?

7. What was the name of Rodney's wife?

8. In the 2001 Christmas special, on which game show presented by Jonathan Ross was Del a contestant?

9. What was the name of Del and Raquel's son?

10. On Christmas Day of which year was the final showing of this sitcom – 2001, 2003 or 2005?

KEEPING UP APPEARANCES

11. How many episodes were made during the five series of this sitcom – 34, 44 or 54?

12. Which actress played Hyacinth Bucket?

13. What was the name of Hyacinth's husband?

14. Can you name Hyacinth's neighbours, the couple who were brother and sister?

15. Which actress played Hyacinth's sister Daisy?

16. In which year was the sitcom first aired on the BBC –1990, 1992 or 1994?

17. Who wrote this sitcom as well as Last of the Summer Wine and Open All Hours?

18. What is the name of Hyacinth's sister, unseen until the final series?

19. What was the name of the vicar played by Jeremy Gittins?

20. Can you name the actress who played the original Rose?

THE OFFICE

21. Which actor played character David Brent?

22. There were two specials, but how many episodes were made over the two series?

23. Who were the two writers of this sitcom?

24. Which actor played Gareth Keenan?

25. What was the name of Dawn Tinsley's boyfriend – Gareth, Keith or Lee?

26. Martin Freeman played the character Tim, but what was his surname?

27. What was the name of the company in the series?

28. What was the name of the travelling sales rep played by Ralph Ineson?

29. True or false: The Office was first broadcast in 2001?

30. What was the theme tune to this sitcom?

DIRECTED BY – 1

Match the sitcom with its director

31.	The Thick of It	Dan Zeff
32.	Porridge	Martin Dennis
33.	People Like Us	Martin Dennis
34.	Fresh Fields	Martin Dennis
35.	Men Behaving Badly	Tony Dow
36.	Man About the House	John Morton
37.	Lee Evans – So What Now?	Peter Frazer-Jones
38.	Ideal (Series 1 and 2)	Armando Iannucci
39.	Coupling	Peter Frazer-Jones
40.	Never Better	Sydney Lotterby

GEORGE AND MILDRED

41.   Can you name the sitcom that featured George and Mildred before this sitcom was made?

42.   How many episodes were made over the five series?

43.   In what year was this sitcom first broadcast?

44.   Can you name the actor who played George Roper?

45.   What was the name of George's pet goldfish?

46.   Can you name the family that lived next door to the Ropers?

47.   Can you name the actress who played Mildred Roper?

48.   Can you name the actor who played George's friend, Gerry?

49.   What was the name of Mildred's dog?

50.   On which TV channel was George and Mildred broad cast?

WRITTEN BY – 1

Match the sitcom with its writer

51.	Carrie and Barry	John Sullivan
52.	Brush Strokes	Andy Hamilton and Guy Jenkin
53.	Watching	Simon Nye
54.	Just Good Friends	Simon Carlyle and Gregor Sharp
55.	Dad's Army	John Esmonde and Bob Larbey
56.	Game On	John Esmonde and Bob Larbey
57.	Going Straight	Jimmy Perry and David Croft
58.	The Good Life	Andrew Davies and Bernadette Davis
59.	Drop the Dead Donkey	Dick Clement and Ian La Frenais
60.	Thin Ice	Jim Hitchmough

ONE FOOT IN THE GRAVE

61. How many episodes were made during the six series?

62. What was Mrs Warboys' Christian name?

63. Which actress played Margaret Meldrew?

64. Who wrote this sitcom?

65. Which actor and presenter played the Meldrews' neighbour Patrick Trench?

66. Where was this sitcom filmed – Christchurch, Colchester or Cardiff?

67. In which year was the final episode broadcast – 2000, 2002 or 2004?

68. Which award did the show win in 1992?

69. What is Victor Meldrew's famous catchphrase?

70. Which job did Victor Meldrew have before retiring?

FAWLTY TOWERS

71. How many episodes were made of this sitcom – 12, 22 or 32?

72. Where was the hotel set – Portsmouth, Torquay or Sheffield?

73. Which actress played Sybil Fawlty?

74. Connie Booth played waitress Polly and she was a student, but what was she studying – English Literature, Art or History?

75. Where was the waiter Manuel from?

76. In what year was this sitcom first broadcast?

77. Can you name the two writers of this sitcom?

78. What colour was the hotel – white, green or yellow?

79. Which actor played hotel manager Basil Fawlty?

80. In what year was the final episode of this sitcom broadcast?

EARLY DOORS

81. How many series of this sitcom were made?

82. In which part of the country was the pub located?

83. Can you name one of the two writers of this comedy?

84. Which TV channel first broadcast the sitcom in May 2003?

85. Which actor played the pub landlord Ken?

86. What is the name of the pub?

87. What is the name of Ken's daughter?

88. Who was Tanya's best friend?

89. True or false: Characters Jean and Winnie are named after the writers' mothers?

90. Which Scottish singer sang the theme tune 'Small World'?

WHICH YEAR? – 1

Match the event with the year it happened

91.	Doctor At Large was first broadcast	1992
92.	Nicholas Lyndhurst was born	1985
93.	Clarence was first broadcast	1916
94.	The final episode of Down the 'Gate was broadcast	1961
95.	Chef! was first broadcast	1998
96.	The final episode of 'Allo 'Allo was broadcast	1971
97.	Reg Varney was born	1976
98.	All In Good Faith was first broadcast	1993
99.	The final episode of Birds of a Feather was broadcast	1990
100.	The final episode of Chelmsford 123 was broadcast	1988

BLACKADDER

101. Can you name two of the three writers of this sitcom?

102. In what year was this sitcom first broadcast on the BBC?

103. A total of 24 episodes of this sitcom were broadcast, but how many series were there?

104. Which actor played the character Baldrick?

105. Rowan Atkinson played Blackadder but was what his Christian name?

106. Who composed the music for this sitcom?

107. Which actor played the character General Melchett?

108. In which century was the first series set – 15th, 16th or 17th

109. In which year was the sitcom last broadcast - 1987, 1988 or 1989?

110. Who produced this sitcom?

DAD'S ARMY

111. Can you name the two writers of this sitcom?

112. True or false: Dad's Army was first broadcast on the BBC in 1968?

113. What was this sitcom originally going to be called?

114. In what fictional seaside town was this sitcom set?

115. Which actor played the character Captain George Mainwaring?

116. What was the name of the theme tune to Dad's Army?

117. How many episodes were shown over the nine series?

118. True or false: Dad's Army won a BAFTA award in 1971 in the 'Best Light Entertainment Production' category?

119. Which actor played the Vicar in 40 Dad's Army episodes?

120. Which character was played by Bill Pertwee?

THE VICAR OF DIBLEY

121. Which former Only Fools and Horses actor played the part of Owen Newitt?

122. Following on from the previous question, what was Owen's job?

123. What is the name of the female vicar played by Dawn French?

124. Following on from the previous question, what is the characters surname?

125. Which character's favourite line is "No, no, no, no, no, yes"?

126. In what year was this sitcom first broadcast on the BBC?

127. Which actress played the character Alice Horton?

128. Which character was the chairman of the Parish Council?

129. In what year was the last episode broadcast, in aid of Comic Relief?

130. True or false: Kylie Minogue once made an appearance in this sitcom?

EPISODES – 1

Match up the sitcom with the number of episodes made

131.	A Bear's Tail	58
132.	The Adventures of Aggie	28
133.	All About Me	6
134.	Brass	6
135.	Butterflies	32
136.	The Brittas Empire	18
137.	Clarence	26
138.	Don't Wait Up	65
139.	Dead Man Weds	39
140.	Drop the Dead Donkey	6

YES MINISTER /
YES, PRIME MINISTER

141. How many episodes were made in total?

142. Can you name the two writers of this sitcom?

143. On which channel was this sitcom broadcast – BBC1, BBC2 or ITV?

144. Which actor played the character Jim Hacker MP?

145. In which decade was this sitcom broadcast – 1970s, 1980s or 1990s?

146. Who composed the theme music for this sitcom?

147. Which chacter played Jim Hacker's Principal Private Secretary, Bernard Woolley?

148. What was the name of Jim Hacker's wife – Annie, Barbara or Charlotte?

149. Which artist drew the opening titles that provided distinctive caricatures of the main characters?

150. Which actor played the character Sir Humphrey Appleby?

PORRIDGE

151. In which prison was this sitcom based?

152. What was Norman Fletcher's middle name?

153. Who was Fletcher's cellmate?

154. Which crime did Fletcher commit, resulting in a five-year sentence?

155. In 1978, which follow-up series was made starring Ronnie Barker?

156. What were the names of the two prison officers, played by Brian Wilde and Fulton Mackay?

157. Which actor played McLaren?

158. Can you name the character that Christopher Biggins played in this sitcom?

159. What the name of Fletcher's daughter who used to visit him on a regular basis, played by Patricia Brake?

160. Which real-life prison was used as the set for the Porridge film in 1979?

OPEN ALL HOURS

161.   What was Granville's relationship with Arkwright – nephew, son or good friend?

162.   Which actress played Nurse Gladys Emmanuel?

163.   What kind of shop did Arkwright own – grocery shop, DIY shop or newsagent?

164.   Which legendry actor played Arkwright?

165.   Can you name Arkwright's Christian name?

166.   This sitcom was first shown in 1973 (the pilot), but when was the last one broadcast?

167.   Which actor played Granville?

168.   True or false: Nurse Gladys Emmanuel appeared in 25 out of the 26 episodes?

169.   How many episodes were there in the first series – 5, 6 or 7?

170.   Can you name the actress who played Mrs Blewett, appearing in 7 out of the 26 episodes?

THE GOOD LIFE

171. How many episodes were made during the four series?

172. In the United States The Good Life was retitled. What did they call it?

173. What was Margo and Jerry's surname?

174. On which channel was this sitcom shown – BBC1, BBC2 or Channel 4?

175. Which character was played by Felicity Kendal?

176. On which birthday did Tom Good give up his job as a draughtsman?

177. Following on from the previous question, for which company did Tom and neighbour Jerry work?

178. In which decade was this sitcom first broadcast – 1960s, 1970s or 1980s?

179. What did the Goods call their two pigs?

180. What was the name of the wine that the Goods made?

CHARACTERS – 1

*Match up the character with the actor/actress
that starred in the role*

181. **Del Trotter (Only Fools and Horses)**   **Tony Britton**

182. **Warren (Porridge)**   **John Le Mesurier**

183. **Ben Harper (My Family)**   **Julia McKenzie**

184. **Jacko (Brush Strokes)**   **Robert Lindsay**

185. **Ria Parkinson (Butterflies)**   **David Jason**

186. **Sergeant Wilson (Dad's Army)**   **Karl Howman**

187. **Toby Latimer (Don't Wait Up)**   **Wendy Craig**

188. **Duncan Waring
(Doctor in the House)**   **Noel Dyson**

189. **Nanny (Father Ted)**   **Sam Kelly**

190. **Hester Fields (Fresh Fields)**   **Robin Nedwell**

FATHER TED

191. Which band provided the instrumental 'Songs of Love' for the opening theme tune?

192. On which channel was this sitcom broadcast – BBC2, ITV or Channel 4?

193. Who was the priests' manic housekeeper – Mrs Doyle, Mrs Smith or Mrs Norton?

194. How many series were made of this sitcom – 2, 3 or 4?

195. Which character shouted "Drink!", "Feck!", "Arse!" and "Girls!" on a regular basis?

196. Can you recall the name of the first ever episode?

197. Which TV presenter appeared in this sitcom playing character Father Noel Furlong?

198. Which actor played Father Ted Crilly?

199. What is the name of the island on which they lived?

200. In which decade was this sitcom made and broadcast?

'ALLO 'ALLO

201. Of what business was René the owner – a café, a bakery or a public house?

202. In what year was 'Allo 'Allo last broadcast?

203. What nationality was René Artois?

204. Which actress played René's wife, Edith Melba Artois?

205. What was the name of the waitress played by actress Vicki Michelle?

206. Can you name the four languages spoken in this sitcom?

207. Who was the leader of the local French Resistance?

208. How many episodes were made over the nine series – 85, 90 or 95?

209. Which character replaced waitress Maria Recamier in the fourth series up until series 9?

210. Which character often used the catchphrase "Good moaning"?

LAST OF THE SUMMER WINE

211. In which year was this sitcom first shown on BBC1 – 1972, 1973 or 1974?

212. Which award did the show win in 1999?

213. What was Compo's real character name?

214. Which character was played by June Whitfield in series 27, 28 and 29?

215. Which actor starred in this sitcom as 'Foggy' Dewhurst and also played Mr Barrowclough in Porridge?

216. Which character was played by Nora Batty?

217. True or false: this is the longest-running sitcom ever in the world?

218. Which character was played by Juliette Kaplan?

219. Which actor played Compo?

220. In 2003, which former George and Mildred and Man About the House star joined the crew on Last of the Summer Wine?

FILMING LOCATIONS – 1

Match up the sitcom with its filming location

221. **Gavin & Stacey (Gavin's house)**

    Tresillian Way, Walkford, Bournemouth

222. **Keeping Up Appearances (Hyacinth's house)**

    Holmfirth, Yorkshire

223. **One Foot in the Grave (Meldrew's house)**

    Whitemead House, Duckmore Road, Bristol

224. **The Vicar of Dibley (exterior shots)**

    Slough

225. **Only Fools and Horses (exterior of Nelson Mandela House)**

    Ringwood, Hampshire

226. **Last of the Summer Wine**

    Michell Close, Stoke Aldermoor, Coventry

227. **Hi-de-Hi!**

    Heather Road, Binley Woods, Coventry

228. **The Office (opening sequence)**

    Trinity Street, Barry, South Glamorgan

229. **Keeping Up Appearances (Daisy & Onslow's house)**

    Warners Holiday Camp, Dovercourt, Essex

230. **The Brittas Empire (leisure centre and exterior shots)**

    Turville, Buckinghamshire

STEPTOE AND SON

231. Can you name the two writers of this sitcom?

232. In which 'Lane' did the Steptoes live?

233. True or false: Elton John took his middle name, Hercules, from the Steptoes' horse?

234. Which famous catchphrase did Harold say to his father, Albert?

235. How many series of the sitcom were made – 8, 9 or 10?

236. Which actor played Albert Steptoe?

237. In what trade were the Steptoes – art dealers, rag and bone men or failing actors?

238. What is the name of the famous theme tune to this sitcom, composed by Ron Grainer?

239. In which year was this sitcom first broadcast – 1960, 1961 or 1962?

240. Which political party did Harold support – Labour, Conservatives or Liberal Democrats?

MEN BEHAVING BADLY

241. Which character did actress Caroline Quentin play?

242. Which pop star appeared in a very brief sequence that was included in Comic Relief during 1997, entitled 'Men Behaving Very Badly Indeed'?

243. What was Tony's surname – Gold, Smart or Perfect?

244. Who created and wrote this sitcom?

245. Which channel took over the show from the ITV after the first two series?

246. Gary was the manager of a small security company. Can you name the two employees at his office?

247. Who was Gary's flatmate in series one, played by Harry Enfield?

248. Which character was played by Leslie Ash?

249. What did Gary's girlfriend do for a living?

250. In which series did Tony and Deborah develop a romance?

ABSOLUTELY FABULOUS

251. Which character is played by Joanna Lumley?

252. Where in London do Edina and her daughter Saffron live?

253. In what year was this sitcom first aired?

254. What is the name of this sitcom's theme tune, written by Bob Dylan and Rick Danko and performed by Julie Driscoll and Adrian Edmondson?

255. What was the title of the first ever episode of this sitcom?

256. Which former Terry and June and Carry On actress played Mother?

257. Edwina changed her name to Edina and was then mostly called Eddy. Who are the only two people who still called her Edwina?

258. Who is Saffron's best friend?

259. Which comedian, screenwriter and actress created this sitcom?

260. How many series were made of this sitcom – 5, 6 or 7?

CHARACTERS – 2

Match up the character with the actor/actress
who starred in the role

261.	Diana Trent (Waiting for God)	**Barry Evans**
262.	Jerry Leadbetter (The Good Life)	**Caroline Quentin**
263.	Manuel (Fawlty Towers)	**Stephanie Cole**
264.	Daphne Warrender (Just Good Friends)	**Paul Venables**
265.	Richard Bucket (Keeping Up Appearances)	**Larry Lamb**
266.	Jeremy Brown (Mind Your Language)	**Andrew Sachs**
267.	Jamie Callender (May to December)	**Sylvia Kay**
268.	Dorothy (Men Behaving Badly)	**Tony Robinson**
269.	Baldrick (Blackadder)	**Paul Eddington**
270.	Mick Shipman (Gavin & Stacey)	**Clive Swift**

RED DWARF

271. True or false: there were nine series of this sitcom?

272. What is Dave Lister obsessed with eating?

273. Which award did Red Dwarf win in 1994 for the best BBC sitcom?

274. Dave Lister, together with which only other character, appeared in all 52 episodes of the show?

275. On which channel was this sitcom originally broadcast – BBC1, BBC2 or BBC3?

276. Can you name the three colours in the Red Dwarf's logo?

277. How long is the Red Dwarf spaceship?

278. Which character is played by Craig Charles?

279. How many light years is the mining ship Red Dwarf from Earth?

280. Which award did the show win in 1994 for an episode from the sixth series, 'Gunmen of the Apocalypse'?

THE ROYLE FAMILY

281. The sitcom follows a working-class family from which city in the UK?

282. True or false: Sue Johnston, who plays Barbara, had to take up smoking herbal cigarettes for the role despite giving up smoking in 1978?

283. Which Oasis song is the theme tune to this sitcom?

284. The first series led up to which big event?

285. Which character, played by Jessica Hynes, is padded out with a 'fat suit', as the actress is much slimmer than the character in real life?

286. Who is the father of the Royle family, played by Ricky Tomlinson?

287. Where does Barbara Royle work on a part-time basis, as the only wage earner?

288. What are the names of Dave's parents?

289. In what year was this sitcom originally broadcast?

290. Which actress plays the role of Denise?

ARE YOU BEING SERVED?

291. This sitcom was based in the men's and women's department or which fictional department store?

292. This sitcom was first broadcast in 1972, but in which year was it last broadcast on BBC1?

293. With whom did Mr Humphries live?

294. What was the most common phrase usually used by Captain Peacock to other staff?

295. At what fictional Spanish resort was the Are You Being Served? film set?

296. Which actor played Mr Humphries, the camp senior assistant in the menswear department?

297. Ten series of this sitcom were made and broadcast, but how many episodes were there – 59, 69 or 79?

298. Following on from the previous question, can you name three of the five actors that appeared in every episode?

299. Who owned the department store?

300. Which actor played Mr Lucas?

POT LUCK – 1

301. In which sitcom, started in 2004, does beautician Jill, upon discovering that her husband Terry is dying of cancer, tell everyone that he has died and then pursues her neighbour, Don, a doctor whose wife is suffering from MS?

302. On which channel was Peep Show originally broadcast – ITV, Channel 4 or Channel 5?

303. What was the name of the fictional company in The Rag Trade, which was first broadcast in 1961 and ran through to 1978?

304. What was the name of the 2004 sitcom that was aired on ITV, lasted for one series and starred comedian Frank Skinner?

305. Which sitcom, first broadcast in 2009, starred Roger Lloyd Pack and featured old boys Tom and Roy who live together and lust over their neighbour Sally?

306. How many series were there of Only When I Laugh, which was shown between 1979 and 1982?

307. Which sitcom, lasting for 3 series, had a character called Jean Price, who was a Labour MP entering the Houses of Parliament for the first time after a by-election?

308. Which sitcom, lasting for 2 series, was shown in the late 1950s and featured Archie Andrews, a ventriloquist's dummy?

309. Which sitcom starred Richard Beckinsale, Paula Wilcox and Robin Nedwell, lasted for 2 series and was first shown in 1970?

310. How many series were there of My Hero?

TO THE MANOR BORN

311. This sitcom was originally aired between 1979 and 1981, but in which year did the show come back with a Christmas special – 2005, 2007 or 2009?

312. Who created this sitcom?

313. Which actress played Marjory Frobisher?

314. In the third episode of the first series, what does Audrey have problems with in her home?

315. True or false: the characters Audrey and Richard are the only ones that appear in all 22 episodes of the show?

316. What was Richard DeVere – a property developer, a farmer or a supermarket owner?

317. Can you name the actors who play Audrey and Richard?

318. What was the name of the village in the show?

319. In the recent Christmas special, what were Richard and Audrey celebrating?

320. On which day of the week was this show aired between 1979 and 1981?

SOME MOTHERS DO 'AVE 'EM

321.　What was the name of Frank Spencer's wife?

322.　How many episodes were made of this sitcom – 22, 27 or 32?

323.　Which actress played Frank Spencer's wife?

324.　What was Frank's main catchphrase?

325.　What can't Frank seem to keep for longer than a day?

326.　In which decade was this sitcom originally shown – 1970s, 1980s or 1990s?

327.　Can you name the person who did all of Frank Spencer's stunts?

328.　True or false: one of the impressions that David Brent performs in The Office, which actually makes his colleagues laugh, is of Frank Spencer?

329.　Can you name the two very famous actors who were originally first and second choice for the role of Frank Spencer before Michael Crawford was given the part?

330.　What was the name of Frank's daughter?

THE LIKELY LADS

331. How many series were there of this sitcom, comprising 21 episodes?

332. Which actor played Bob Ferris?

333. What was the name of the new canteen manageress that Terry fancied in the third episode?

334. In the first episode of the second series, with whom did Bob and Terry have dates – a couple of nurses, a couple of air stewardesses or a couple of supermarket operatives?

335. What was the name of Terry's older sister?

336. Why did Terry keep away from Bob for three weeks during the final series?

337. At the end of the final series, Bob wanted to join the Army but was rejected - why?

338. Which actor played Terry Collier?

339. What was the name of the factory where Bob and Terry worked?

340. What was the name of the popular sequel series to this sitcom?

EPISODES – 2

Match up the sitcom with the number of episodes made

341.	Doctor At Large	49
342.	Ever Decreasing Circles	19
343.	Early Doors	42
344.	Filthy, Rich and Catflap	29
345.	Father, Dear Father	64
346.	Father Ted	6
347.	Gimme, Gimme, Gimme	12
348.	Love Thy Neighbour	25
349.	Only Fools and Horses	27
350.	One Foot in the Grave	55

MY FAMILY

351. Which actor, who played Nick, later appeared in BT television commercials?

352. What is the family surname?

353. In which series did Ben and Susan's niece Abi join the sitcom – 2nd, 3rd or 4th?

354. Which actress plays Susan?

355. Where in the UK is the family home?

356. Can you name all three of Ben and Susan's children?

357. What is Ben's occupation?

358. Which university did Janey attend, but later dropped out?

359. In what year was My Family first broadcast on BBC1?

360. What number is the family's house on Lancaster Road?

DROP THE DEAD DONKEY

361.   At what fictional TV news company was this sitcom based?

362.   Which award did the show win in 1994 for the Best Comedy (Programme or Series)?

363.   Do you know what the sitcom was to be called before it was changed to Drop the Dead Donkey?

364.   Which character is the star reporter who is always trying to make his stories as sensational as possible?

365.   How many episodes were broadcast over the six series?

366.   Character Alex Pates left the news company to work where?

367.   What is the name of the station's editor, who is nervous wreck?

368.   In which decade was this sitcom broadcast – 1980s, 1990s or 2000s?

369.   What secret did Helen Cooper keep from her daughter and her parents?

370.   Which character is the Chief Executive of the company, and a yes man to owner Sir Roysten Merchant?

RISING DAMP

371. Who is the tenant that Rigsby repeatedly tries to seduce?

372. What is Rigsby's Christian name?

373. How many series were there of this sitcom, comprising 28 episodes?

374. In which decade was this sitcom originally shown?

375. What was the name of Rigsby's cat?

376. Where in the UK was the sitcom set – Yorkshire, Lincolnshire or Nottinghamshire?

377. Tenant Phillip claimed to be the son of an African tribal king when he arrived, but where was he really from?

378. Which character was played by Frances de la Tour?

379. What was tenant Alan's occupation – a researcher, a medical student or a photographer?

380. Richard Beckinsale, who played Alan, was featuring and involved in the filming of which other sitcom whilst appearing in this one?

CHARACTERS – 3

*Match up the character with the actor/actress
who starred in the role*

381.	Walter (For the Love of Ada)	Peter Jones
382.	Tyler Boyce (The Green Green Grass)	Martin Freeman
383.	Gladys Pugh (Hi-de-Hi!)	Wilfred Pickles
384.	Gladys Emmanuel (Open All Hours)	Michael Burns
385.	Oliver Smallbridge (Never the Twain)	Lynda Baron
386.	Tim Canterbury (The Office)	Lesley Joseph
387.	Harold Fenner (The Rag Trade)	Sally Geeson
388.	Dorien Green (Birds of a Feather)	Windsor Davies
389.	Sally Abbott (Bless This House)	Ruth Madoc
390.	Colin Weatherby (The Brittas Empire)	Jack Doolan

DINNERLADIES

391. How many series of this sitcom were made and broadcast?

392. What was the name of the canteen manager?

393. All filming was done entirely in the canteen of which fictional factory?

394. What was the name of Dolly's best friend?

395. Who both created and starred in this sitcom?

396. The canteen manager is in love with which dinnerlady?

397. In the first series, what theme was used for the Christmas party - a Japanese theme, a Chinese theme or a Scottish theme?

398. Which character is the youngest member of the team?

399. What relationship is Petula to Bren –her daughter, her sister or her mother?

400. Which character did former Coronation Street actress Thelma Barlow play?

AS TIME GOES BY

401.   Which very popular actress played the role of Jean?

402.   Jean's daughter Judith was married twice and both marriages ended in divorce. Can you name her two ex-husbands?

403.   Who was Lionel's publisher, who later in the sitcom became Judith's third husband?

404.   What was the name of Jean's secretary and Judith's best friend?

405.   When Jean retired from her company, where did she do some voluntary work?

406.   Where in the UK did Lionel and Jean live together?

407.   What was the title of Lionel's book?

408.   Which actor played Lionel?

409.   In which year was this sitcom first broadcast – 1991, 1992 or 1993?

410.   What was the name of Jean's secretarial agency?

TEACHERS

411.   How many episodes were made and broadcast over the four series?

412.   In which decade was this sitcom broadcast – 1980s, 1990s or 2000s?

413.   Where in the UK was the state school based?

414.   What was Clare's secretary and personal assistant called?

415.   What was the name of the school before it merged with another school in the fourth series to form Wattkins School?

416.   On which channel was this sitcom broadcast – ITV, Channel 4 or Channel 5?

417.   What was the name of the PE teacher, who later became a geography teacher?

418.   Who celebrated their birthday in the first episode?

419.   During series four Bob gets very excited about meeting his new Thai bride, but what was her name?

420.   What was the name of the Head of English at Wattkins School, who joined in the fourth series?

THE YOUNG ONES

421. Who was the landlord played by actor Alexei Sayle?

422. True or false: Many external scenes were filmed in Bristol but the sitcom was set in North London?

423. What was the name of the college that the four students attended?

424. How many episodes of this sitcom were made and broadcast – 12, 21 or 121?

425. Which actor played the clinically depressed hippy Neil Pye?

426. Which subject was Rick studying?

427. Which singer did Rick admire?

428. What was the name of the medical student, the orange-haired, punk rocker played by Adrian Edmondson?

429. Which well-known comedian and actor made a guest appearance as a postman in the final episode entitled 'Summer Holiday'?

430. On which channel was this sitcom originally broadcast?

TILL DEATH US DO PART

431. This sitcom was based around which family?

432. True or false: this show was on the screen for 10 years?

433. Which sitcom was a sequel to this one?

434. Which political party did Alf support?

435. Alf referred to his Liverpudlian son-in-law as what?

436. Alf was a fan of which London football team?

437. How many series were made – 6, 7 or 8?

438. What was the name of Alf and Else's daughter?

439. Alf referred to his wife as what – silly cow, silly moo or silly goat?

440. Where in the UK was this sitcom based?

BUTTERFLIES

441. How many episodes were made and broadcast over the four series?

442. What were the names of Ria and Ben's two sons?

443. In what year was this sitcom originally broadcast?

444. Where does the title come from?

445. Which actress played Ria?

446. On which channel was this sitcom broadcast – BBC1, BBC2 or ITV?

447. Who wrote this sitcom?

448. What was the name of the theme tune, which was written and originally recorded by Dolly Parton?

449. True or false: Nicholas Lyndhurst plays one of Ria and Ben's sons?

450. Can you recall Ria and Ben's surname?

THE THIN BLUE LINE

451.   True or false: this sitcom was only broadcast for a year?

452.   Who wrote this sitcom?

453.   Which former Love Thy Neighbour actor played Constable Frank Gladstone?

454.   Which character is played by Rowan Atkinson?

455.   How many series were made – 2, 3 or 4?

456.   Can you recall the name of the police station?

457.   Which character is second in command to her husband, who is the inspector?

458.   Why did the inspector receive a letter from the BBC in the second series?

459.   Which actor played Constable Kevin Goody?

460.   Who was the head of the CID unit at the police station?

THE FALL AND RISE OF
REGINALD PERRIN

461. In which decade was this sitcom first broadcast?

462. What was the name of Reginald's wife, played by actress Pauline Yates?

463. At what number house on Coleridge Close in London did Reginald live?

464. What was the name of the company where Reginald worked as a sales executive?

465. In the second series, Reginald remarried his wife and started a business, but what was it called?

466. Which actor played Reginald Perrin?

467. When Reginald faked his own suicide by what name did he call himself?

468. What was the name of the sequel, which lasted for one series (seven episodes)?

469. Which actress, who plays Audrey in Coronation Street, played secretary Joan Greengross?

470. Can you recall the name of Reginald's son?

PETER KAY'S PHOENIX NIGHTS

471. What is the name of the working men's club?

472. Following on from the previous question, where in the UK is the club located?

473. On which channel was this sitcom originally broadcast?

474. This sitcom was a spin-off from which spoof documentary series?

475. What award did this sitcom win at the 2002 British Comedy Awards?

476. In what year did this sitcom first hit the screen?

477. Which character was the club owner, played by actor Peter Kay?

478. Which real-life TV presenter opened the club in the first episode of this sitcom?

479. What was the name of the rival club owned by Den Perry, played by actor Ted Robbins?

480. Which character was the resident DJ and rocked the club with sounds of Aled Jones's 'Walking in the Air' during the opening night?

WAITING FOR GOD

481.   Where was this sitcom set – in a school, in a church or in a retirement home?

482.   Which actress played Diana Trent?

483.   Where in the UK was this sitcom based?

484.   What was Tom Ballard's profession before retiring?

485.   What is the name of the manager at Bayview?

486.   In which decade was this sitcom broadcast?

487.   On which channel was this sitcom originally broadcast?

488.   Which character was forever harassing the female residents and bragging about his innumerable conquests?

489.   In which series did Tom and Diana get together as a couple?

490.   How many episodes were broadcast over the five series?

CHARACTERS – 4

*Match up the character with the actor/actress
who starred in the role*

491.	Gwen West (Gavin & Stacey)	Sharon Horgan
492.	April (Hi-de-Hi!)	Reginald Marsh
493.	Humphrey (George and Mildred)	Paul Barber
494.	Alfie Butts (My Family)	Miranda Raison
495.	Phil Parker (Parents of the Band)	Doug Fisher
496.	Donna (Pulling)	Linda Regan
497.	Linsey (Plus One)	Melanie Walters
498.	Denzil Tulser (Only Fools and Horses)	David Ryall
499.	Frank Morrison (Outnumbered)	Rhodri Meilir
500.	Larry Simmonds (Man About the House)	Jimmy Nail

BIRDS OF A FEATHER

501. What was Sharon and Chris' surname?

502. Can you name Tracey's noisy neighbour?

503. Why were Chris and Darryl sent to prison in the first episode?

504. Where in Essex did Tracey and Darryl buy their expensive house?

505. How many episodes were broadcast between 1989 and 1998 – 82, 92 or 102?

506. What was the name of Tracey and Darryl's son?

507. Who was Dorien's husband, whom she consistently cheated on with other men?

508. Which actress played Sharon?

509. What is the name of the theme tune by Irving Berlin?

510. What was Sharon and Tracey's relationship?

BREAD

511. In which decade was the first episode broadcast – 1970s, 1980s or 1990s?

512. What was the name of the family in this sitcom?

513. Where in the UK did the family live?

514. Following on from the previous question, the family lived at Kelsall Street, but can you name the street that was shown at the start of each episode?

515. Can you name Nellie's five children?

516. With whom did Freddie, Nellie's husband, have an affair?

517. How many series were made of this sitcom, comprising 74 episodes in total?

518. Who created and wrote this sitcom – Carla Lane, Ronald Wolfe or Vince Powell?

519. What character was played by Jonathon Morris?

520. Nellie and her children, who took it in turns, visited and delivered meals to their next-door neighbour – who was that?

THE LEAGUE OF GENTLEMEN

521. On which channel was this sitcom originally broadcast?

522. In which fictional village in the north of England was this sitcom based?

523. In what year was this sitcom first broadcast?

524. Which two characters ran the local shop?

525. Can you recall the name of the local priest?

526. Who directed both the series and the film?

527. Following on from the previous question, can you name the title of the film?

528. Can you name two of the four writers of this sitcom?

529. How many series were there of this comedy?

530. Can you recall the name of the very unsympathetic doctor?

NEVER THE TWAIN

531. Which actor played Simon Peel?

532. True or false: Oliver and Simon were next-door neighbours?

533. How many series of this sitcom were made and broad cast – 11, 12 or 13?

534. Oliver and Simon shared the same profession – what was that?

535. When Oliver and Simon's children got married, which country did they move to together?

536. In which year was this sitcom last broadcast – 1991, 1992 or 1993?

537. Which actor played Ringo and appeared in nearly two-thirds of the TV series?

538. True or false: the actors who played Oliver and Simon were the only two characters that appeared in every episode of this show?

539. Which actress played Mrs Sadler?

540. Can you recall the title of the first episode – 'A Night at the Opera', 'Families at War' or 'Of Meissen Men'?

BRITISH SITCOMS

Rearrange the letters to reveal the name of a sitcom

541.   ENO OOTF NI HET VEARG

542.   YONL OOFLS DNA SSROHE

543.   HET FFEICO

544.   DMBEINRO

545.   ETH TTSRIAB PEMRIE

546.   RBDEDAKLAC

547.   SBSAR

548.   RREPODIG

549.   YLLEEHS

550.   EIFL FO LEIYR

JUST GOOD FRIENDS

551. On which channel was this sitcom broadcast – BBC1, BBC2 or Channel 4?

552. Can you name the two successful sitcoms that John Sullivan wrote before Just Good Friends?

553. This sitcom was originally broadcast in 1983, but in what year was the last episode run?

554. How many episodes were made and broadcast – 22, 32 or 42?

555. What was character Penny's surname?

556. Can you name the actress that played Penny's mother Daphne?

557. In 1984 a Christmas special was made (intended to be the last episode, but another 7 followed) in which Penny left the UK for a new job where – Paris, Rome or Munich?

558. Which character did Paul Nicholas play in this sitcom?

559. True or false: Paul Nicholas sang the theme tune, written by John Sullivan and arranged by Ronnie Hazlehurst?

560. Can you name the actress that played Penny?

DIRECTED BY – 2

Match the sitcom with its director

561.	The Smoking Room	Ray Butt
562.	Thin Ice	Peter Frazer-Jones
563.	Watching	Sylvie Boden
564.	To the Manor Born	Tristram Shapeero
565.	Spaced	Gareth Carrivick
566.	George and Mildred	Gareth Gwenlan
567.	For the Love of Ada	Les Chatfield
568.	Citizen Smith	Sarah Smith
569.	Faith in the Future	Ronnie Baxter
570.	Feel the Force	Edgar Wright

2.4 CHILDREN

571.   What was the family's surname?

572.   In which decade was this sitcom broadcast – 1980s, 1990s or 2000s?

573.   To what did the title of this sitcom refer?

574.   Can you name the actress that played the family's friend Rona?

575.   What kind of business did Bill run?

576.   How many series were made of this sitcom?

577.   On which channel was this sitcom broadcast?

578.   What kind of business did Ben run?

579.   Can you name the creator and writer of this successful sitcom?

580.   What was the colour of the show title when the sitcom first started – red, blue or yellow?

BOTTOM

581.   Where in London did Richie and Eddie live?

582.   In what year did Bottom first hit the screen?

583.   Which comedy pair created and starred in this sitcom?

584.   True or false: this sitcom was originally broadcast on BBC1?

585.   In which year was the last episode (the 18th) shown – 1994, 1995 or 1996?

586.   From whose will did Richie receive £600 in the first series?

587.   Which character was played by Christopher Ryan?

588.   Where, in the second series, did Richie and Eddie go camping?

589.   In the first series, on what did Eddie spend their £11.80 dole money?

590.   True or false: there were five live theatre shows as a spin-off from the television series?

IT AIN'T HALF HOT MUM

591.   When the sitcom was launched in 1974, what year was it in the story?

592.   Which two comedy writers wrote and created this sitcom?

593.   True or false: Windsor Davies starred as the Sergeant Major?

594.   Who was the youngest member of the concert party?

595.   Gunner 'Nosher' Evans was usually doing what?

596.   Which character did actor George Layton play in the first and second series?

597.   What was the name of the first ever episode?

598.   Who was the leader of the concert party?

599.   In what year was this sitcom broadcast for the last time?

600.   How many episodes were broadcast – 46, 56 or 66?

THE BRITTAS EMPIRE

601. Can you name the fictional leisure centre that was the setting for the show?

602. Which actor played Gordon Brittas?

603. In which decade was this sitcom broadcast?

604. What was the name of Gordon's wife?

605. How many episodes were broadcast over the seven series – 53, 54 or 55?

606. Can you recall the name of the first ever episode?

607. What was Gordon Brittas's middle name?

608. What were the names of Carole's three children?

609. What was the name of Gordon Brittas's next door neighbour?

610. Which actor played Colin Weatherby?

GIMME, GIMME, GIMME

611.   How many series were made of this sitcom?

612.   Can you recall the theme tune, sung by Abba?

613.   True or false: this show was filmed in front of a live studio audience at The London Studios?

614.   What colour was Linda's hair?

615.   What was Linda's surname?

616.   What was the profession of Linda's flatmate Tom Farrell?

617.   Following on from the previous question, at the end of series three Tom left the flat as he'd got his big break in a television soap - which one?

618.   At what number at Paradise Passage, Kentish Town, did Linda and Tom live?

619.   Following on from the previous question, what was the name of their landlord, played by Rosalind Knight?

620.   Can you name the couple that lived together in the other flat rented out by their landlady?

MR BEAN

621.   Who plays Mr Bean?

622.   How many episodes were there of this sitcom – 14, 34 or 54?

623.   In the first episode Mr Bean goes to a church service, but he only knows and is able to sing which two words?

624.   With whom does Mr Bean live in his flat?

625.   Following on from the previous question, where in the UK does Mr Bean live?

626.   What make of car did Mr Bean drive?

627.   Can you name Mr Bean's girlfriend, played by actress Matilda Ziegler?

628.   Mr Bean stayed in a posh hotel in episode 8, but what was the number of his room?

629.   Who crushed Mr Bean's car while he was attending the local school's open day?

630.   Can you name either one of Mr Bean's two friends, who were invited for New Year's Eve celebrations but left before 12 o'clock and went to another party next door?

BROADCASTING CHANNELS

Match up the sitcom with the channel on which it was aired

631.	Only Fools and Horses	ITV
632.	Man About the House	BBC1
633.	Extras	BBC1
634.	Never the Twain	BBC1
635.	Ever Decreasing Circles	BBC2
636.	Rising Damp	BBC1
637.	Dad's Army	ITV
638.	Love Thy Neighbour	BBC1
639.	Till Death Us Do Part	ITV
640.	The Vicar of Dibley	ITV

EPISODES – 3

Match up the sitcom with the number of episodes made

641.	Please, Sir!	12
642.	Rab C. Nesbitt	13
643.	The Rag Trade	14
644.	Surgical Spirit	19
645.	Seconds Out	27
646.	Spaced	52
647.	15 Storeys High	50
648.	2.4 Children	55
649.	Yus, My Dear	57
650.	Whatever Happened to the Likely Lads?	59

GOODNIGHT SWEETHEART

651. In which decade was this sitcom made and broadcast?

652. Can you recall Gary's surname?

653. What was the name of the pub where Gary met Phoebe, when he went back in time to wartime in London?

654. When Gary went back in time, what did he claim to be?

655. How did Gary's wife Yvonne become a millionairess?

656. Who was the policeman that Gary became friends with in the 1940s?

657. Can you name the two actresses that played Phoebe, one from series 1 to 3 and the other from series 4 to 6?

658. Which former Only Fools and Horses actor played Gary?

659. True or false: in the final episode, on VE Day, Gary discovered that the time portal had now closed and he was trapped in the 1940s for good?

660. What was the name of Gary's best friend, who would always cover for him?

BLESS THIS HOUSE

661. The last episode was broadcast in 1976, but in what year was this sitcom first broadcast?

662. What was the family's surname?

663. Can you name the two neighbours played by Anthony Jackson and Patsy Rowlands?

664. What was Sid's job?

665. What were Sid and Jean's two children called?

666. Who was one of the creators and writers of this sitcom, who released his autobiography From Rags to Gags in 2008?

667. At which television studios was this sitcom recorded?

668. Which actor played Sid Abbott?

669. How many episodes were made of this sitcom – 55, 65 or 75?

670. Who produced this sitcom, and later presented the game show Fifteen to One?

THE GREEN GREEN GRASS

671. In what year was this sitcom first broadcast?

672. Boycie was on the run from which infamous London villains when he moved to the farm?

673. Can you name the three staff that came with the farm when Boycie and Marlene moved there?

674. Which Welsh neighbour, played by Alan David, took an instant dislike to Boycie?

675. True or false: boxer Ricky Hatton made a guest appearance in this sitcom?

676. What is the name of Boycie's son – Tyler, Tim or Terry?

677. In what part of the UK is this sitcom set?

678. Which actress played Imelda Cakeworthy?

679. In the second series, Boycie sought to be elected as what?

680. Which character was played by actor David Ross?

NEAREST AND DEAREST

681. How many of the 46 episodes were shown in colour – 24, 26 or 28?

682. What was the name of Joshua Pledge's small pickle business?

683. Which actress played Nellie?

684. Can you name the two comedy writers that created this sitcom?

685. True or false: this sitcom was shown on BBC1?

686. Where in the UK was this sitcom based?

687. What was the name of the carthorse?

688. What was the name of second cousin Lily's husband?

689. Who was the toothless and capped Pledge's foreman, played by Joe Gladwin?

690. What was the name of Nellie's brother?

ON THE BUSES

691. Can you name the two creators of this sitcom?

692. Which actor played Stan Butler?

693. What was the name of the bus company that Stan, Jack and Blakey worked for?

694. What was the name of Stan's brother-in-law, who was married to Stan's sister Olive?

695. What was inspector Blake's first name?

696. In what year was this sitcom first broadcast on ITV?

697. What was the most used catchphrase that Blakey said to Stan?

698. Can you name the three films that were made in 1971, 1972 and 1973?

699. Which actor played Jack Harper?

700. How many series were made of this sitcom – 7, 10 or 13?

FIRST BROADCAST

Match up the sitcom with the year in which it was first broadcast

701.	Nighty Night	1981
702.	Surgical Spirit	1980
703.	Game On	1991
704.	Hi-De-Hi!	2004
705.	Joking Apart	1988
706.	The Old Guys	1989
707.	Never the Twain	1979
708.	You Rang, M'Lord?	1990
709.	Only When I Laugh	2009
710.	No Job for a Lady	1995

ROBIN'S NEST

711. What was the name of Robin's girlfriend?

712. Following on from the previous question, what was the name of the actress who played Robin's girlfriend?

713. In which part of London was Robin's bistro?

714. What was the name of the one-armed Irishman?

715. Following on from the previous question, what was the actor's name?

716. True or false: Richard O'Sullivan wrote the theme tune for this sitcom, which was performed by Brian Bennett?

717. Who was Robin's business partner?

718. How many series were made of this sitcom – 6, 7 or 8?

719. On which channel was this sitcom originally broadcast – BBC2, ITV or Channel 4?

720. True or false: this sitcom was a spin-off from Man About the House?

ACTORS & ACTRESSES

*Name the actor/actress who played the character
in each sitcom*

721. Detective Inspector Derrick Grim (The Thin Blue Line)

722. Bryn West (Gavin & Stacey)

723. Marlene Boyce (The Green Green Grass)

724. Peggy Ollerenshaw (Hi-de-Hi!)

725. Sally (The Old Guys)

726. Vince Clark (15 Storeys High)

727. Mr Frank Pickle (The Vicar of Dibley)

728. Mrs Jean Warboys (One Foot in the Grave)

729. Rachel (The Magnificent Evans)

730. Sal Vine (Jam and Jerusalem)

GAME ON

731. At what apartment number did Matthew, Martin and Mandy live at 23 Wellington Road, Battersea, London during series one?

732. Following on from the previous question, what number was the flat on series two and three – 53, 54 or 55?

733. Can you name Martin's Irish girlfriend?

734. What was the colour of Martin's hair?

735. What did Matthew have a fear of?

736. Who was Mandy's boss who later died on his wedding day to her?

737. What was the name of Mandy's best friend?

738. Which actress played Mandy Wilkins and later appeared in EastEnders as Ronnie Mitchell?

739. Matthew Malone was played by Neil Stuke in all the series of this sitcom except the first. Who first played Matthew?

740. What was the name of the theme tune?

GAVIN & STACEY

741. What is Gavin's surname?

742. Gavin is a Tottenham fan but which London team does his best friend Smithy support?

743. What is Smithy's Christian name?

744. Which actress plays Nessa?

745. In which year was this sitcom originally broadcast – 2006, 2007 or 2008?

746. Can you name the two locations, where both the families live, in which the sitcom is mainly based?

747. What is the name of Stacey's brother, played by actor Robert Wilfort?

748. True or false: this sitcom won the 'Best New British TV Comedy' award at the British Comedy Awards 2007?

749. How many times was Stacey engaged before marrying Gavin?

750. Which actress plays Stacey and also appeared in the 2003 film Love Actually?

GRACE AND FAVOUR

751. This was a sequel to which sitcom?

752. How many series were made of this sitcom?

753. What was the Christian name of Mrs Slocombe, played by Mollie Sugden?

754. True or false: this sitcom ran on television for three years during the 1990s?

755. Wendy Richard, who played Miss Brahms, took time off from which soap in order to film episodes of this sitcom?

756. The staff took over and worked at which manor?

757. What was the name of Mrs Slocombe's pussycat?

758. Which character was played by Frank Thornton?

759. True or false: in the last episode Wendy Richard's cairn terrier, named 'Shirley Brahms', made a cameo appearance?

760. Where in the UK were the external shots for the series taken?

EXTRAS

761. True or false: Ricky Gervais won a BAFTA award in 2007 for the Best Comedy Performance in Extras?

762. The closing title track is 'Tea for the Tillerman', but who wrote and performed this song?

763. Which actor has never appeared in this sitcom – Ronnie Corbett, Samuel L. Jackson or Tom Cruise?

764. What was the name of Ricky Gervais's character, a film extra, in this sitcom?

765. Which comedy actor first appeared as the guest on the sitcom, attempting to direct a film based on the plight of a young man named Goran?

766. Where did the agent for Ricky Gervais's character work before becoming an agent?

767. Which Harry Potter actor starred in the third episode of the second series?

768. Which actress played Maggie Jacobs, who later appeared in Ugly Betty?

769. Who wrote and directed this sitcom with Ricky Gervais and also played character Darren Lamb?

770. Ricky Gervais's character and Les Dennis worked on which pantomime together during the first series?

BRUSH STROKES

771. What was the name of Lionel Bainbridge's wife, who had a crush on Jacko?

772. Who owned the pub that Jacko would often visit?

773. What was the name of the theme tune, written and performed by Kevin Rowland and Dexys Midnight Runners?

774. How many episodes were made – 40, 50 or 60?

775. Who played Jacko and was the only actor to appear in every episode of this show?

776. What was Jacko's profession?

777. Who was Jacko's best friend?

778. On which channel was this sitcom broadcast – BBC1, BBC2 or ITV?

779. Can you recall the name of the company that Jacko unsuccessfully started, towards the end of the show, which Elmo then turned into a wine bar?

780. Can you name the secretary at work who became Jacko's fiancée in series two?

NOT GOING OUT

781. Which BAFTA-winning comic created this sitcom?

782. Which character died in only the second episode of the first series?

783. In the second series, which sophisticated entrepreneur in his fifties was Lucy's boss and then became her boyfriend?

784. At the start of the second series, Lee's former flatmate Kate moved back to which country?

785. Which character was Tim's dim girlfriend?

786. Tim is which character's best friend?

787. On which channel was this sitcom aired – BBC1, ITV or Channel 4?

788. Where was the flat located – London, Manchester or Liverpool?

789. Who was Lucy and Lee's flat cleaner?

790. Which actor and comedian played Tim Adams?

POT LUCK - 2

791. Which sitcom started in January 2009 and starred Caroline Quentin and Neil Dudgeon?

792. During 2008, Last of the Summer Wine broadcast which series for the first time - their 27th, 29th or 31st?

793. Which sitcom lasted for 6 episodes, was broadcast in 1980 on BBC1, and featured disaster-prone Ken Archer, who lost his job and his wife on the same day?

794. In which 1980s sitcom did vicar Philip Lambe ask the Bishop for a transfer from an easy job in a quiet, wealthy suburban parish to a more challenging one in an inner-city parish?

795. In which decade was Beggar My Neighbour first broadcast?

796. Which sitcom started in 2007 and is about the lives of five teenagers living in Abingdon?

797. Which BBC sitcom, broadcast in 1987, starred Rik Mayall, Adrian Edmondson and Nigel Planer, lasting only one 6-episode series?

798. In which year did Faith in the Future first hit the TV screen?

799. Which sitcom, written by A. David Nobbs and shown on ITV between 1980 and 1982, starred two girls who quit their day jobs in search of glamour?

800. Which sitcom, written by Ronald Wolfe and Ronald Chesney, was shown in the 1960s, ran for 5 series and starred Thora Hird and Freddie Frinton?

FRESH FIELDS

801. How many episodes were made and broadcast of this sitcom – 17, 27 or 37?

802. What was the surname of William and Hester?

803. Who lived in the granny flat attached to William and Hester's house?

804. Which character used to pop round to borrow items from William and Hester?

805. Following on from the previous question, what was this character's catchphrase, the only catchphrase in this sitcom, as she walked in the house?

806. In the final episode William took a job in which country?

807. Which actress played Hester?

808. Which character wore glasses – William or Hester?

809. In which decade was this sitcom made and broadcast?

810. Which actor played William?

AFTER YOU'VE GONE

811. Which former Only Fools and Horses star played Jimmy Venables?

812. Following on from the previous question, what was Jimmy's occupation?

813. Can you name Jimmy's two children?

814. Can you name Jimmy's girlfriend, who is his hairdresser and also works as a barmaid?

815. Can you name the occupation of Jimmy's mother-in-law, Diana Neal?

816. Jimmy's ex-wife went to which country in order for him to move back into the marital home to look after his two children?

817. What is the name of Jimmy's local pub, run by landlord Bobby?

818. Which actress played Diana Neal?

819. In the last episode of series three, what does Jimmy buy off of the Internet?

820. Can you name the creator of this sitcom?

LOVE THY NEIGHBOUR

821. Can you name the two creators of this sitcom?

822. In which decade was this sitcom broadcast – 1960s, 1970s or 1980s?

823. Can you name the black couple that moved next door to Eddie and Joan Booth?

824. Which football team did Eddie support?

825. Can you name the actor who played Eddie's neighbour, who later starred in EastEnders as Patrick?

826. What did Eddie's neighbour often call him?

827. Which actor played Eddie?

828. How many episodes were broadcast – 55, 58 or 61?

829. Which political party did Bill support –Conservative, Labour or Liberal Democrat?

830. Can you name the actress who played Barbie Reynolds?

MAN ABOUT THE HOUSE

831.   Which television company made this sitcom?

832.   Which football team did Robin Tripp support?

833.   Can you name the year this sitcom was first broadcast?

834.   What was Chrissy's surname?

835.   Which character was played by actor Brian Murphy?

836.   Where did Jo and Chrissy find their future flatmate Robin?

837.   Can you name George's friend who was a builder and schemer?

838.   Which actor played the character Robin Tripp?

839.   What was the name of George's wife?

840.   What did Robin do for a living?

SORRY!

841. When the sitcom started in 1981, how old was the character Timothy Lumsden, who was still living with his mother?

842. What was the name of Timothy's mother?

843. What was Timothy's profession?

844. On which channel was this sitcom originally broadcast?

845. What was the name of Timothy's sister, played by Marguerite Hardiman?

846. Which very well known actor played Timothy Lumsden?

847. How many episodes were broadcast over the seven series – 36, 43 or 50?

848. In which year was this sitcom last broadcast – 1988, 1989 or 1990?

849. What was the first episode called – 'For Love or Mummy', 'For Love or Money' or 'For Love or Many'?

850. What phrase did Sydney Lumsden, Timothy's father, say to Timothy when he felt Timothy had said something inappropriate?

SHELLEY

851. Who was Shelley's girlfriend?

852. There were 71 episodes of this sitcom made, in how many series?

853. What was Shelley's Christian name?

854. Which actor played Shelley?

855. Which character did Josephine Tewson play?

856. True or false: this sitcom ran from 1979 until 1992?

857. Who created this sitcom - Peter Tilbury, Vince Powell or Harry Driver?

858. On which channel was this sitcom originally broadcast – BBC1, ITV or Channel 4?

859. With whom did Shelley share a house during the final two series?

860. Following on from the previous question, why was the house the only one left in the street?

TERRY AND JUNE

861.   What was Terry and June's surname?

862.   In which programme did Terry Scott and June Whitfield begin their television partnership in 1968?

863.   How many episodes were made – 65, 85 or 105?

864.   Terry and June lived at which number house in Popular Avenue, Purley, Surrey?

865.   What was the name of Terry's nephew?

866.   In the first two series what were the names of Terry and June's neighbours?

867.   In what year was this sitcom last broadcast, having started in 1979?

868.   In which year was June Whitfield upgraded to a CBE – 1996, 1997 or 1998?

869.   True of false: the BBC put a feature-length film, entitled Terry and June - The Movie, into production, but it was never made?

870.   For which company did Terry work?

TWO PINTS OF LAGER AND A PACKET OF CRISPS

871.   Where in the UK is this sitcom based?

872.   Which actor played the character Jonny Keogh in the first six series?

873.   In what year did this sitcom first hit the TV screen?

874.   Which character left and become a cruise singer?

875.   What was Jonny's favourite food?

876.   What star sign was Donna – Scorpio, Leo or Gemini?

877.   Which character was played by former Hollyoaks actor Will Mellor?

878.   What was the name of the first ever episode?

879.   Which series was broadcast in 2009 – 6th, 7th or 8th?

880.   Who found out that she was adopted and that her biological dad was gay?

WHICH YEAR? – 2

Match the event with the year it happened

881.	Big Top first broadcast	1986
882.	Maureen Lipman was born	2008
883.	Faith in the Future was last broadcast	2004
884.	Love Thy Neighbour was last broadcast	1980
885.	Full House finished broadcasting after 20 episodes	1983
886.	Harry H. Corbett sadly passed away	1946
887.	Yootha Joyce sadly passed away	1976
888.	Shane, starring Frank Skinner, was first broadcast	1982
889.	Beautiful People was first broadcast	1986
890.	Only Fools and Horses won its first BAFTA Award for the best comedy series	2009

COUPLING

891. There were four series of this sitcom, but how many episodes – 18, 28 or 38?

892. Which character normally says the completely wrong thing at the wrong time?

893. Which job does Jane hold?

894. Sally, played by actress Kate Isitt, supports which political party?

895. Can you name one of the two nicknames Susan gives to Patrick?

896. Who is Sally's best friend?

897. In which year was this sitcom first broadcast – 1998, 1999 or 2000?

898. Who created this sitcom?

899. In series four, with which character does Susan have a baby boy – Steve, Jeff or Patrick?

900. Which character runs a local science fiction media store called Hellmouths?

IN SICKNESS AND IN HEALTH

901.   This was a sequel to which two sitcoms, the first running from 1966 until 1975 and the other in 1981?

902.   Which actor played Alf Garnett?

903.   Where in the UK was the sitcom based?

904.   Which character, played by Eamonn Walker, helped with the housework and caring for Else?

905.   Following on from the previous question, what nick name did Alf Garnett give him?

906.   How many episodes of this sitcom were broadcast – 47, 57 or 67?

907.   Which double act wrote and performed the theme tune?

908.   What was the name of Alf and Else's daughter, played by Una Stubbs?

909.   In which year was this sitcom last broadcast on BBC1 – 1990, 1992 or 1994?

910.   Which football team did Alf Garnett support?

WRITTEN BY – 2

Match the sitcom with its writer

911.	Roman's Empire	Vince Powell
912.	The Rag Trade	Harry Williams and Jack Williams
913.	Are You Being Served?	Susan Nickson and Daniel Peak
914.	Bottom	David Renwick
915.	Not On Your Nellie	Johnny Speight
916.	Two Pints of Lager and a Packet of Crisps	Jeremy Lloyd and David Croft
917.	Till Death Us Do Part	Ronald Chesney and Ronald Wolfe
918.	One Foot in the Grave	Jeremy Lloyd and David Croft
919.	Mind Your Language	Tom Brennand and Roy Bottomley
920.	Grace and Favour	Adrian Edmondson and Rik Mayall

MIND YOUR LANGUAGE

921. Who created this sitcom?

922. How many episodes were broadcast – 32, 37 or 42?

923. In what year was the sitcom first broadcast on ITV?

924. What was the name of the English teacher?

925. What was the name of the first ever episode?

926. The fourth series, broadcast in 1986, was filmed at which college?

927. Which character did Albert Moses play?

928. Can you name the actress that played Danielle Favre, a French au pair who got a lot of male attention in the sitcom?

929. Which actress played the character Jamila Ranjha?

930. Can you name the principal's name?

THREE UP, TWO DOWN

931.   When Nick and Angie had their baby, what did they decide to rent out?

932.   Can you recall the neighbour's name?

933.   This sitcom ran for four years, but in what year was it first broadcast?

934.   Which character was played by Michael Elphick?

935.   Can you name three of the four actors that appeared in all 25 episodes of this sitcom?

936.   What was Sam's occupation?

937.   What was the first ever episode called?

938.   Who wrote this sitcom?

939.   Which character was played by Angela Thorne?

940.   What was Nick's occupation – a policeman, a photographer or a magazine editor?

YOU RANG, M'LORD?

941. This sitcom ran for 26 episodes, but how many series were made?

942. Which actor played the character Alf Stokes?

943. In which decade was this sitcom set – 1920s, 1940s or 1960s?

944. Which comedian, actor and later presenter sang the theme tune for this sitcom?

945. Who was the master of the house, played by actor Donald Hewlett?

946. Following on from the previous question, can you name his two daughters in this sitcom?

947. Which actor played the character PC Wilson?

948. Which two comedy writers created this sitcom?

949. Where in the UK was this sitcom filmed – Suffolk, Essex or Norfolk?

950. In what year did this sitcom first hit the TV screen?

GALTON & SIMPSON

951.   In what year did the pair meet at Milford Sanatorium where they were both undergoing treatment for TB?

952.   Which radio sitcom did the pair start writing in 1954?

953.   What were the pair awarded in 2000 for their contribution to British television?

954.   Which very popular sitcom did the pair write about two rag and bone men?

955.   Following on from the previous question, what award did they win in 1962 and 1963 for the best TV comedy, also being runners-up in 1964 and 1965?

956.   What TV series did they write that starred Leslie Phillips in 1973?

957.   Can you name the titles of the two films that were released in 1972 and 1973?

958.   What was the name of the television series they wrote in 1961 for Sid James to star in?

959.   What are Galton and Simpson's Christian names?

960.   Who is older – Galton or Simpson?

WATCHING

961.   How many series of the sitcom were made and broadcast – 7, 8 or 9?

962.   Which actor played Malcolm?

963.   Which actress, who played Brenda Wilson in this sitcom, also sang the theme tune 'What Does He See in Me?'?

964.   Where in the UK was this sitcom set?

965.   What was Malcolm's surname?

966.   Which actor played Terry Milton, later appearing in EastEnders as Billy Mitchell?

967.   The sitcom title referred to a game that Brenda and her sister Pamela, and later Brenda and Malcolm, played in the pub – what was it?

968.   On which channel was this sitcom broadcast?

969.   What was Malcolm's hobby, which Brenda often got involved with too?

970.   What happened in the final episode, broadcast in April 1993?

BENIDORM

971. Which actress played Madge?

972. Who wrote this sitcom, having also co-written The Catherine Tate Show?

973. In what year was this sitcom first broadcast on ITV?

974. What is the name of the holiday resort where this sitcom is based?

975. Which character was known as 'The Oracle'?

976. Following on from the previous question, which comedy actor played this role?

977. True or false: Benidorm was nominated for a BAFTA in the Best Sitcom category of the 2008 awards?

978. Can you name the real-life hotel in Benidorm where this sitcom was filmed?

979. What was the surname of Mick, Janice, Chantelle and Michael?

980. True or false: former EastEnders actress Wendy Richard starred in two episodes during the second series?

MAY TO DECEMBER

981.   What is Zoe's profession?

982.   What are the names of Alec's two children?

983.   Where did Alec and Zoe meet each other?

984.   Where in the UK was this sitcom based – Leeds, London or Liverpool?

985.   Can you name the two secretaries that worked in Alec's office before Rosie arrived in the final series?

986.   How many series of this sitcom were made and broadcast – 4, 6 or 8?

987.   What is Alec Callender's profession?

988.   Which actor played Alec?

989.   What name did Alec and Zoe give their baby girl in the fifth series?

990.   On which channel was this sitcom last broadcast – BBC1, BBC2 or ITV?

LAST BROADCAST

**Match up the sitcom with the year in which
it was last broadcast**

991.	The Worker	1991
992.	Up Pompeii!	1998
993.	That's My Boy	2007
994.	Shelley	1970
995.	On the Buses	1961
996.	Is It Legal?	1986
997.	How Do You Want Me?	1992
998.	Brush Strokes	1978
999.	The Army Game	1973
1000.	Sensitive Skin	1999

ANSWERS

ONLY FOOLS AND HORSES

1. *Yellow*
2. *Peckham*
3. *7*
4. *1981*
5. *Trigger*
6. *Lennard Pearce*
7. *Cassandra*
8. *The Goldrush*
9. *Damien*
10. *2003*

KEEPING UP APPEARANCES

11. *44*
12. *Patricia Routledge*
13. *Richard*
14. *Elizabeth and Emmett*
15. *Judy Cornwell*
16. *1990*
17. *Roy Clarke*
18. *Violet*
19. *Michael*
20. *Shirley Stelfox*

THE OFFICE

21. *Ricky Gervais*
22. *12*
23. *Ricky Gervais and Stephen Merchant*
24. *Mackenzie Crook*
25. *Lee*
26. *Canterbury*

27. Wernham Hogg

28. Chris Finch (Finchy)

29. True

30. 'Handbags and Gladrags'

DIRECTED BY – 1

31.	The Thick of It	Armando Iannucci
32.	Porridge	Sydney Lotterby
33.	People Like Us	John Morton
34.	Fresh Fields	Peter Frazer-Jones
35.	Men Behaving Badly	Martin Dennis
36.	Man About the House	Peter Frazer-Jones
37.	Lee Evans – So What Now?	Tony Dow
38.	Ideal (Series 1 and 2)	Dan Zeff
39.	Coupling	Martin Dennis
40.	Never Better	Martin Dennis

GEORGE AND MILDRED

41. Man About the House

42. 38

43. 1976

44. Brian Murphy

45. Moby

46. The Fourmiles

47. Yootha Joyce

48. Roy Kinnear

49. Truffles

50. ITV

WRITTEN BY – 1

| 51. | Carrie and Barry | Simon Nye |

52.	Brush Strokes	John Esmonde and Bob Larbey
53.	Watching	Jim Hitchmough
54.	Just Good Friends	John Sullivan
55.	Dad's Army	Jimmy Perry and David Croft
56.	Game On	Andrew Davies and Bernadette Davis
57.	Going Straight	Dick Clement and Ian La Frenais
58.	The Good Life	John Esmonde and Bob Larbey
59.	Drop the Dead Donkey	Andy Hamilton and Guy Jenkin
60.	Thin Ice	Simon Carlyle and Gregor Sharp

ONE FOOT IN THE GRAVE

61. 42
62. Jean
63. Annette Crosbie
64. David Renwick
65. Angus Deayton
66. Christchurch
67. 2000
68. BAFTA for best comedy
69. "I don't believe it!"
70. Security guard

FAWLTY TOWERS

71. 12
72. Torquay

73. *Prunella Scales*

74. *Art*

75. *Barcelona*

76. *1975*

77. *John Cleese and Connie Booth*

78. *White*

79. *John Cleese*

80. *1979*

EARLY DOORS

81. *2*

82. *Manchester*

83. *Craig Cash and Phil Mealey*

84. *BBC2*

85. *John Henshaw*

86. *The Grapes*

87. *Melanie*

88. *Debbie*

89. *True: Craig Cash's mum is named Jean and Phil Mealey's mum is named Winnie*

90. *Roddy Frame*

WHICH YEAR? – 1

91. **Doctor At Large was first broadcast** *1971*

92. **Nicholas Lyndhurst was born** *1961*

93. **Clarence was first broadcast** *1988*

94. **The final episode of Down the 'Gate was broadcast** *1976*

95. **Chef! was first broadcast** *1993*

96. **The final episode of 'Allo 'Allo was broadcast** *1992*

97. **Reg Varney was born** *1916*

98. **All In Good Faith was first broadcast** *1985*

99.   *The final episode of Birds of a Feather
was broadcast*   *1998*

100.   *The final episode of Chelmsford 123
was broadcast*   *1990*

BLACKADDER

101.   *Richard Curtis, Ben Elton and Rowan Atkinson*

102.   *1983*

103.   *4*

104.   *Tony Robinson*

105.   *Edmund*

106.   *Howard Goodall*

107.   *Stephen Fry*

108.   *15th*

109.   *1989*

110.   *John Lloyd*

DAD'S ARMY

111.   *Jimmy Perry and David Croft*

112.   *True*

113.   *The Fighting Tigers*

114.   *Walmington-on-Sea*

115.   *Arthur Lowe*

116.   *'Who do you think you are kidding, Mr Hitler?'*

117.   *80*

118.   *True*

119.   *Frank Williams*

120.   *A.R.P. Warden Hodges*

THE VICAR OF DIBLEY

121.   *Roger Lloyd Pack*

122.   Local farmer (and Parish Council member)

123.   Geraldine

124.   Granger

125.   Jim Trott

126.   1994

127.   Emma Chambers

128.   Cllr David Horton MBE

129.   2007

130.   True

EPISODES - 1

131.	A Bear's Tail	6
132.	The Adventures of Aggie	26
133.	All About Me	18
134.	Brass	32
135.	Butterflies	28
136.	The Brittas Empire	58
137.	Clarence	6
138.	Don't Wait Up	39
139.	Dead Man Weds	6
140.	Drop the Dead Donkey	65

YES MINISTER / YES, PRIME MINISTER

141.   38: 22 (3 series) then 16 (2 series)

142.   Anthony Jay and Jonathan Lynn

143.   BBC2

144.   Paul Eddington

145.   1980s (1980-84 and 1986-87)

146.   Ronnie Hazlehurst

147.   Derek Fowlds

148.   Annie

149.   Gerald Scarfe

150.   Nigel Hawthorne

PORRIDGE

151.   Slade Prison

152.   Stanley

153.   Lennie Godber

154.   Theft (he stole a lorry)

155.   Going Straight

156.   Mr Barrowclough and Mr Mackay

157.   Tony Osoba

158.   Lukewarm

159.   Ingrid Fletcher

160.   Chelmsford Prison, Essex

OPEN ALL HOURS

161.   Nephew

162.   Lynda Baron

163.   Grocery shop

164.   Ronnie Barker

165.   Albert

166.   1985

167.   David Jason

168.   True

169.   6

170.   Kathy Staff

THE GOOD LIFE

171.   30

172.   Good Neighbors

173.   Leadbetter

174.   BBC1

175.   Barbara Good

176.   40th

177.   JMM

178.   1970s (1975-78)

179.   Pinky and Perky

180.   Peapod Burgundy

CHARACTERS - 1

181.	Del Trotter (Only Fools and Horses)	David Jason
182.	Warren (Porridge)	Sam Kelly
183.	Ben Harper (My Family)	Robert Lindsay
184.	Jacko (Brush Strokes)	Karl Howman
185.	Ria Parkinson (Butterflies)	Wendy Craig
186.	Sergeant Wilson (Dad's Army)	John Le Mesurier
187.	Toby Latimer (Don't Wait Up)	Tony Britton
188.	Duncan Waring (Doctor in the House)	Robin Nedwell
189.	Nanny (Father Ted)	Noel Dyson
190.	Hester Fields (Fresh Fields)	Julia McKenzie

FATHER TED

191.   The Divine Comedy

192.   Channel 4

193.   Mrs Doyle

194.   3

195.   Father Jack Hackett

196.   'Good Luck, Father Ted'

197.   Graham Norton

198.   Dermot Morgan

199.   Craggy Island

200.   1990s (1995-98)

'ALLO 'ALLO

201.   A café

202.   1992

203.   French

204.   Carmen Silvera

205.   Yvette Carte-Blanche

206.   French, German, Italian and English

207.   Michelle "of the Resistance" Dubois

208.   85

209.   Mimi Labonq

210.   Officer (Captain) Crabtree (played by Arthur Bostrom)

LAST OF THE SUMMER WINE

211.   1973

212.   The National Television Award for Most Popular Comedy
       Programme

213.   William 'Compo' Simmonite

214.   Nelly

215.   Brian Wilde

216.   Kathy Staff

217.   True

218.   Pearl

219.   Bill Owen

220.   Brian Murphy

FILMING LOCATIONS

221.   Gavin & Stacey (Gavin's house)   Trinity Street,
                                         Barry, South Glamorgan

222.   Keeping Up Appearances
       (Hyacinth's house)   Heather Road, Binley
                                         Woods, Coventry

223.	One Foot in the Grave	
	(Meldrew's house)	Tresillian Way, Walkford, Bournemouth
224.	The Vicar of Dibley	
	(exterior shots)	Turville, Buckinghamshire
225.	Only Fools and Horses	
	(exterior of Nelson Mandela House)	Whitemead House, Duckmore Road, Bristol
226.	Last of the Summer Wine	Holmfirth, Yorkshire
227.	Hi-de-Hi!	Warners Holiday Camp, Dovercourt, Essex
228.	The Office (opening sequence)	Slough
229.	Keeping Up Appearances	
	(Daisy & Onslow's house)	Michell Close, Stoke Aldermoor, Coventry
230.	The Brittas Empire	
	(leisure centre and exterior shots)	Ringwood, Hampshire

STEPTOE AND SON

231. Ray Galton and Alan Simpson

232. Oil Drum Lane (a fictional street in Shepherd's Bush, London)

233. True

234. "You dirty old man"

235. 8

236. Wilfrid Brambell

237. Rag and bone men

238. 'Old Ned'

239. 1962

240. Labour

MEN BEHAVING BADLY

241. **Dorothy**

242. **Kylie Minogue**

243. **Smart**

244. **Simon Nye**

245. **BBC1**

246. **Anthea and George**

247. **Dermot**

248. **Deborah**

249. **Dorothy was a nurse**

250. **Series 6 (the last series)**

ABSOLUTELY FABULOUS

251. **Patsy Stone**

252. **Holland Park**

253. **1992**

254. **'This Wheel's on Fire'**

255. **'Fashion'**

256. **June Whitfield**

257. **Her mother and her ex-husband Justin**

258. **Sarah**

259. **Jennifer Saunders**

260. **5**

CHARACTERS - 2

261. **Diana Trent (Waiting for God)**   **Stephanie Cole**

262. **Jerry Leadbetter (The Good Life)**   **Paul Eddington**

263. **Manuel (Fawlty Towers)**   **Andrew Sachs**

264. **Daphne Warrender (Just Good Friends)**   **Sylvia Kay**

265. **Richard Bucket (Keeping Up Appearances)** **Clive Swift**

266. **Jeremy Brown (Mind Your Language)**   **Barry Evans**

267.	Jamie Callender (May to December)	Paul Venables
268.	Dorothy (Men Behaving Badly)	Caroline Quentin
269.	Baldrick (Blackadder)	Tony Robinson
270.	Mick Shipman (Gavin & Stacey)	Larry Lamb

RED DWARF

271. False: there were eight

272. Curries

273. British Comedy Award

274. The Cat

275. BBC2

276. White, black and red

277. 6 miles

278. Dave Lister

279. 3 million

280. International Emmy Award in the Popular Arts category

THE ROYLE FAMILY

281. Manchester

282. True

283. 'Half the World Away'

284. Denise and Dave's wedding

285. Cheryl

286. Jim Royle

287. At a local bakery

288. Dave and Jocelyn Best

289. 1998

290. Caroline Aherne

ARE YOU BEING SERVED?

291. Grace Brothers

292. 1985

293. His mother

294. "Are you free?"

295. Costa Plonka

296. John Inman

297. 69

298. Mollie Sugden (Mrs Slocombe), John Inman (Mr Humphries),
      Frank Thornton (Captain Peacock), Wendy Richard (Miss
      Brahms) and Nicholas Smith (Mr Rumbold)

299. 'Young' Mr Grace

300. Trevor Bannister

POT LUCK – 1

301. Nighty Night

302. Channel 4

303. Fenner Fashions

304. Shane

305. The Old Guys

306. 4

307. No Job for a Lady

308. Educating Archie

309. The Lovers

310. 6

TO THE MANOR BORN

311. 2007

312. Peter Spence

313. Angela Thorne

314. Her heating

315. True

316. A supermarket owner

317. Penelope Keith and Peter Bowles

318. Grantleigh, Somerset (near the fictional town of Marlbury)

319. Their (25th) silver wedding anniversary

320. Sunday

SOME MOTHERS DO 'AVE 'EM

321. Betty

322. 22

323. Michele Dotrice

324. "Ooh Betty"

325. A job

326. 1970s (1973-78)

327. Michael Crawford, who played Frank Spencer

328. True

329. Ronnie Barker and Norman Wisdom

330. Jessica

THE LIKELY LADS

331. 3

332. Rodney Bewes

333. Freda

334. A couple of nurses

335. Audrey Collier

336. Bob had chicken pox

337. Due to his flat feet

338. James Bolam

339. Ellison's Electrical

340. Whatever Happened to the Likely Lads?

EPISODES - 2

341. Doctor At Large   29

342.	Ever Decreasing Circles	27
343.	Early Doors	12
344.	Filthy, Rich and Catflap	6
345.	Father, Dear Father	49
346.	Father Ted	25
347.	Gimme, Gimme, Gimme	19
348.	Love Thy Neighbour	55
349.	Only Fools and Horses	64
350.	One Foot in the Grave	42

MY FAMILY

351.	Kris Marshall
352.	Harper
353.	3rd
354.	Zoë Wanamaker
355.	Chiswick, West London
356.	Nick, Janey and Michael
357.	A dentist
358.	Manchester University
359.	2000
360.	78

DROP THE DEAD DONKEY

361.	Globelink News
362.	BAFTA TV Award
363.	'Dead Belgians Don't Count'
364.	Damien Day
365.	65
366.	The BBC
367.	George Dent
368.	1990s (1990-98)

369. *That she is a lesbian*

370. *Gus Hedges*

RISING DAMP

371. *Miss Ruth Jones*

372. *Rupert*

373. *4*

374. *1970s (1974-78)*

375. *Vienna*

376. *Yorkshire*

377. *Croydon*

378. *Miss Jones*

379. *A medical student*

380. *Porridge*

CHARACTERS - 3

381. *Walter (For the Love of Ada)*   **Wilfred Pickles**

382. *Tyler Boyce (The Green Green Grass)*   **Jack Doolan**

383. *Gladys Pugh (Hi-de-Hi!)*   **Ruth Madoc**

384. *Gladys Emmanuel (Open All Hours)*   **Lynda Baron**

385. *Oliver Smallbridge (Never the Twain)*   **Windsor Davies**

386. *Tim Canterbury (The Office)*   **Martin Freeman**

387. *Harold Fenner (The Rag Trade)*   **Peter Jones**

388. *Dorien Green (Birds of a Feather)*   **Lesley Joseph**

389. *Sally Abbott (Bless This House)*   **Sally Geeson**

390. *Colin Weatherby (The Brittas Empire)*   **Michael Burns**

DINNERLADIES

391. *2*

392. *Tony Martin*

393. *HWD Components*

394. *Jean*

395. *Victoria Wood*

396. *Bren*

397. *A Japanese theme*

398. *Twinkle*

399. *Her mother*

400. *Dolly Bellfield*

AS TIME GOES BY

401. *Judi Dench*

402. *Chris and Ben*

403. *Alistair Deacon*

404. *Sandy*

405. *A charity shop*

406. *Holland Park, London*

407. *My Life in Kenya*

408. *Geoffrey Palmer*

409. *1992*

410. *Type for You*

TEACHERS

411. *40*

412. *2000s (2001-04)*

413. *Bristol*

414. *Liz Webb*

415. *Summerdown Comprehensive*

416. *Channel 4*

417. *Brian Steadman*

418. *Simon*

419. *Ping*

420. *Ewan Doherty*

THE YOUNG ONES

421.   Jerzei Balowski

422.   True

423.   Scumbag College

424.   12

425.   Nigel Planer

426.   Sociology (domestic sciences)

427.   Cliff Richard

428.   Vyvyan Basterd

429.   Lenny Henry

430.   BBC2

TILL DEATH US DO PART

431.   The Garnett family

432.   True (1965-75)

433.   Till Death.... (and then In Sickness and in Health)

434.   Conservative Party

435.   A randy Scouse git

436.   West Ham United

437.   7

438.   Rita

439.   Silly moo

440.   East End of London

BUTTERFLIES

441.   28

442.   Adam and Russell

443.   1978

444.   Ben collects butterflies

445.   Wendy Craig

446.   BBC2

447.   *Carla Lane*

448.   *'Love Is Like A Butterfly'*

449.   *True*

450.   *Parkinson*

THE THIN BLUE LINE

451.   *True (November 1995-December 1996)*

452.   *Ben Elton*

453.   *Rudolph Walker*

454.   *Inspector Raymond Fowler*

455.   *2*

456.   *Gasforth Police Station*

457.   *Sergeant Patricia Dawkins*

458.   *They wanted to make a fly-on-the-wall documentary about Gasforth Police Station*

459.   *James Dreyfus*

460.   *Detective Inspector Derek Grim*

THE FALL AND RISE OF REGINALD PERRIN

461.   *1970s (1976-79)*

462.   *Elizabeth Perrin*

463.   *12*

464.   *Sunshine Desserts*

465.   *Grot*

466.   *Leonard Rossiter*

467.   *Martin Wellbourne*

468.   *The Legacy of Reginald Perrin*

469.   *Sue Nicholls*

470.   *Mark*

PETER KAY'S PHOENIX NIGHTS

471.   *The Phoenix Club*

472.   **Bolton (Greater Manchester)**

473.   **Channel 4**

474.   **That Peter Kay Thing**

475.   **The People's Choice Award**

476.   **2001**

477.   **Brian Potter**

478.   **Roy Walker**

479.   **The Banana Grove**

480.   **Spencer**

WAITING FOR GOD

481.   **In a retirement home**

482.   **Stephanie Cole**

483.   **Bayview Retirement Village, near Bournemouth**

484.   **Accountant**

485.   **Harvey Baines**

486.   **1990s**

487.   **BBC1**

488.   **Basil Makepeace**

489.   **3rd**

490.   **47**

CHARACTERS - 4

491.	**Gwen West (Gavin & Stacey)**	**Melanie Walters**
492.	**April (Hi-de-Hi!)**	**Linda Regan**
493.	**Humphrey (George and Mildred)**	**Reginald Marsh**
494.	**Alfie Butts (My Family)**	**Rhodri Meilir**
495.	**Phil Parker (Parents of the Band)**	**Jimmy Nail**
496.	**Donna (Pulling)**	**Sharon Horgan**
497.	**Linsey (Plus One)**	**Miranda Raison**
498.	**Denzil Tulser (Only Fools and Horses)**	**Paul Barber**

499.	Frank Morrison (Outnumbered)	David Ryall
500.	Larry Simmonds (Man About the House)	Doug Fisher

BIRDS OF A FEATHER

501. Theodopolopodos

502. Dorien Green

503. They committed armed robbery

504. Chigwell

505. 102

506. Garth

507. Marcus Green

508. Pauline Quirke

509. 'What'll I Do?'

510. They were sisters

BREAD

511. 1980s (the first one in 1986)

512. The Boswell family

513. Liverpool (in the district of Dingle)

514. Elswick Street

515. Joey, Jack, Adrian, Aveline and Billy

516. Lilo Lil

517. 7

518. Carla Lane

519. Adrian

520. Grandad

THE LEAGUE OF GENTLEMEN

521. BBC2

522. Royston Vasey

523. 1999

524.	*Tubbs and Edward Tattsyrup*

525.	*Revd Bernice Woodall*

526.	*Steve Bendelack*

527.	*The League of Gentlemen's Apocalypse*

528.	*Jeremy Dyson, Mark Gatiss, Reece Shearsmith and Steve Pemberton*

529.	*3*

530.	*Dr Ira Carlton*

NEVER THE TWAIN

531.	*Donald Sinden*

532.	*True*

533.	*11*

534.	*They were both antique dealers*

535.	*Canada*

536.	*1991*

537.	*Derek Deadman*

538.	*True*

539.	*Maria Charles*

540.	*'Families at War'*

BRITISH SITCOMS

541.	*One Foot in the Grave*

542.	*Only Fools and Horses*

543.	*The Office*

544.	*Benidorm*

545.	*The Brittas Empire*

546.	*Blackadder*

547.	*Brass*

548..	*Porridge*

549.	*Shelley*

550.   Life of Riley

JUST GOOD FRIENDS

551.   BBC1

552.   Citizen Smith and Only Fools and Horses

553.   1986

554.   22

555.   Warrender

556.   Sylvia Kay

557.   Paris

558.   Vince Pinner

559.   True

560.   Jan Francis

DIRECTED BY - 2

561.	The Smoking Room	Gareth Carrivick
562.	Thin Ice	Sarah Smith
563.	Watching	Les Chatfield
564.	To the Manor Born	Gareth Gwenlan
565.	Spaced	Edgar Wright
566.	George and Mildred	Peter Frazer-Jones
567.	For the Love of Ada	Ronnie Baxter
568.	Citizen Smith	Ray Butt
569.	Faith in the Future	Sylvie Boden
570.	Feel the Force	Tristram Shapeero

2.4 CHILDREN

571.   Porter

572.   1990s

573.   The 'average' size of a UK family

574.   Julia Hills

575.   A catering business

576.   8

577.   BBC1

578.   A heating repair business

579.   Andrew Marshall

580.   Blue

BOTTOM

581.   Hammersmith, West London

582.   1991

583.   Rik Mayall and Adrian Edmondson

584.   False: it was shown on BBC2

585.   1995

586.   His auntie

587.   Dave Hedgehog

588.   Wimbledon Common

589.   A second-hand copy of Parade magazine

590.   True

IT AIN'T HALF HOT MUM

591.   1945

592.   Jimmy Perry and David Croft

593.   True

594.   Gunner 'Parky' Nigel Parkins

595.   Eating

596.   Bombardier 'Solly' Solomons

597.   'Meet the Gang'

598.   Colonel Reynolds

599.   1981

600.   56

THE BRITTAS EMPIRE

601.   Whitbury New Town Leisure Centre

602.   Chris Barrie

603.   1990s (1991-97)

604.   Helen

605.   53

606.   'Laying the Foundations'

607.   Wellesley

608.   Ben, Emily and Jessica

609.   Pam Shields (but Gordon Brittas always called her Pat)

610.   Michael Burns

GIMME, GIMME, GIMME

611.   3

612.   'Gimme! Gimme! Gimme! (A Man After Midnight)'

613.   True

614.   Red

615.   La Hughes

616.   An actor

617.   Crossroads

618.   69

619.   Beryl Merit

620.   Jez and his wife Suze

MR BEAN

621.   Rowan Atkinson

622.   14

623.   "ALLELUIA! ALLELUIA!"

624.   Teddy

625.   Highbury, North London

626.   A Mini

627. Irma Gobb

628. Room 426 (in the episode called 'Mr Bean in Room 426')

629. The Army

630. Rupert and Hubert

BROADCASTING CHANNELS

631.	Only Fools and Horses	BBC1
632.	Man About the House	ITV
633.	Extras	BBC2
634.	Never the Twain	ITV
635.	Ever Decreasing Circles	BBC1
636.	Rising Damp	ITV
637.	Dad's Army	BBC1
638.	Love Thy Neighbour	ITV
639.	Till Death Us Do Part	BBC1
640.	The Vicar of Dibley	BBC1

EPISODES – 3

641.	Please, Sir!	55
642.	Rab C. Nesbitt	52
643.	The Rag Trade	59
644.	Surgical Spirit	50
645.	Seconds Out	13
646.	Spaced	14
647.	15 Storeys High	12
648.	2.4 Children	57
649.	Yus, My Dear	19
650.	Whatever Happened to the Likely Lads?	27

GOODNIGHT SWEETHEART

651. 1990s

652. Sparrow

653. The Royal Oak pub

654. A secret agent and a singer-songwriter

655. Running a successful organic beauty products company

656. Reg Deadman

657. Dervla Kirwan (series 1 to 3) and Elizabeth Carling (series 4 to 6)

658. Nicholas Lyndhurst

659. True

660. Ron

BLESS THIS HOUSE

661. 1971

662. The Abbott family

663. Betty and Trevor

664. A traveling stationery salesman

665. Sally and Mike

666. Vince Powell

667. Thames Television's Teddington Studios

668. Sid James

669. 65

670. William G. Stewart

THE GREEN GREEN GRASS

671. 2005

672. The Driscoll Brothers

673. Elgin, Jed and Bryan

674. Llewellyn

675. True

676. Tyler

677. Oakham, Shropshire

678. *Ella Kenion*

679. *Mayor*

680. *Elgin Sparrowhawk*

NEAREST AND DEAREST

681. *28*

682. *Pledge's Purer Pickles*

683. *Hylda Baker*

684. *Vince Powell and Harry Driver*

685. *False: it was shown on ITV*

686. *Colne, Lancashire*

687. *Storm*

688. *Walter*

689. *Stan Hardman*

690. *Eli*

ON THE BUSES

691. *Ronald Wolfe and Ronald Chesney*

692. *Reg Varney*

693. *Luxton & District Traction Company*

694. *Arthur*

695. *Cyril*

696. *1969*

697. *"I 'ate you, Butler!"*

698. *On the Buses (1971), Mutiny on the Buses (1972) and Holiday on the Buses (1973)*

699. *Bob Grant*

700. *7*

FIRST BROADCAST

701. *Nighty Night*   2004

702.	Surgical Spirit	1989
703.	Game On	1995
704.	Hi-De-Hi!	1980
705.	Joking Apart	1991
706.	The Old Guys	2009
707.	Never the Twain	1981
708.	You Rang, M'Lord?	1988
709.	Only When I Laugh	1979
710.	No Job for a Lady	1990

ROBIN'S NEST

711. Vicky

712. Tessa Wyatt

713. Fulham

714. Albert

715. David Kelly

716. True

717. James Nicholls (his future father-in-law)

718. 6

719. ITV

720. True

ACTORS & ACTRESSES

721. David Haig

722. Rob Brydon

723. Sue Holderness

724. Su Pollard

725. Jane Asher

726. Sean Lock

727. John Bluthal

728. Doreen Mantle

729.   Sharon Morgan

730.   Sue Johnston

GAME ON

731.   7

732.   54

733.   Clare Monahan

734.   Ginger

735.   Going outside

736.   Archie

737.   Claudia

738.   Samantha Janus

739.   Ben Chaplin

740.   'Where I Find My Heaven'

GAVIN & STACEY

741.   Shipman

742.   West Ham United

743.   Neil

744.   Ruth Jones

745.   2007

746.   Billericay in Essex and Barry in Vale of Glamorgan

747.   Jason West

748.   True

749.   6

750.   Joanna Page

GRACE AND FAVOUR

751.   Are You Being Served?

752.   2

753.   Betty

754. *False: it was only on air for one year (January 1992-February 1993)*

755. *EastEnders*

756. *Millstone Manor*

757. *Tiddles*

758. *Captain Stephen Peacock*

759. *True*

760. *Gloucestershire (in and around, and just outside Tetbury)*

EXTRAS

761. *True*

762. *Cat Stevens*

763. *Tom Cruise*

764. *Andy Millman*

765. *Ben Stiller*

766. *Carphone Warehouse*

767. *Daniel Radcliffe*

768. *Ashley Jensen*

769. *Stephen Merchant*

770. *Aladdin*

BRUSH STROKES

771. *Veronica*

772. *Elmo Putney*

773. *Because of You*

774. *40*

775. *Karl Howman*

776. *A painter*

777. *Eric*

778. *BBC1*

779. *Splosh*

780.   *Sandra*

NOT GOING OUT

781.   **Lee Mack**

782.   **Tim's grandmother**

783.   **Guy**

784.   **America**

785.   **Daisy**

786.   **Lee**

787.   **BBC1**

788.   **London**

789.   **Barbara**

790.   **Tim Vine**

POT LUCK - 2

791.   **Life of Riley**

792.   **29th**

793.   **Time of My Life**

794.   **All in Good Faith**

795.   **1960s (1966-68)**

796.   **Coming of Age**

797.   **Filthy, Rich and Catflap**

798.   **1995**

799.   **The Glamour Girls**

800.   **Meet the Wife**

FRESH FIELDS

801.   **27**

802.   **Fields**

803.   **Hester's mother Nancy**

804.   **Sonia Barrett**

805. *"It's only Sonia!"*

806. *France (then another sitcom, French Fields, was made)*

807. *Julia McKenzie*

808. *William*

809. *1980s (1984-86)*

810. *Anton Rodgers*

AFTER YOU'VE GONE

811. **Nicholas Lyndhurst**

812. **A painter and decorator**

813. **Alex and Molly**

814. **Siobhan Casey**

815. **A schoolteacher**

816. **Africa**

817. **The Leek and Shepherd**

818. **Celia Imrie**

819. **A motorbike**

820. **Fred Barron**

LOVE THY NEIGHBOUR

821. **Vince Powell and Harry Driver**

822. **1970s**

823. **Bill and Barbie Reynolds**

824. **Manchester United**

825. **Rudolph Walker**

826. **"White honky" or "Snowflake"**

827. **Jack Smethurst**

828. **55**

829. **Conservative Party**

830. **Nina Baden-Semper**

MAN ABOUT THE HOUSE

831. Thames Television

832. Southampton

833. 1973

834. Plummer

835. George Roper

836. In their bath after a party

837. Jerry

838. Richard O'Sullivan

839. Mildred

840. A student chef

SORRY!

841. 41

842. Phyllis

843. A librarian

844. BBC1

845. Muriel

846. Ronnie Corbett

847. 43

848. 1988

849. 'For Love or Mummy'

850. "Language, Timothy!"

SHELLEY

851. Frances

852. 10

853. James

854. Hywel Bennett

855. Edna Hawkins (Shelley's landlady)

856. True

857. Peter Tilbury

858. ITV

859. Ted Bishop

860. The others had been demolished to make way for a leisure centre

TERRY AND JUNE

861. Medford

862. Scott On

863. 65

864. 71

865. Alan

866. Brian and Tina Pillbeam

867. 1987

868. 1998

869. True

870. Playsafe Fire Extinguishers and Appliances

TWO PINTS OF LAGER AND A PACKET OF CRISPS

871. Runcorn, Cheshire

872. Ralph Little

873. 2001

874. Janet

875. Biscuits

876. Scorpio

877. Gaz Wilkinson

878. 'Fags, Shags and Kebabs'

879. 8th

880. Louise Brooks

WHICH YEAR? – 2

881. Big Top first broadcast   2009

882.	Maureen Lipman was born	1946
883.	Faith in the Future was last broadcast	1983
884.	Love Thy Neighbour was last broadcast	1976
885.	Full House finished broadcasting after 20 episodes	1986
886.	Harry H. Corbett sadly passed away	1982
887.	Yootha Joyce sadly passed away	1980
888.	Shane, starring Frank Skinner, was first broadcast	2004
889.	Beautiful People was first broadcast	2008
890.	Only Fools and Horses won its first BAFTA Award for the best comedy series	1986

COUPLING

891. 28

892. Steve Taylor

893. Traffic reporter for a local radio station

894. Labour

895. 'Donkey' and 'Tripod'

896. Susan Walker

897. 2000

898. Steven Moffat

899. Steve

900. Oliver Morris

IN SICKNESS AND IN HEALTH

901. Till Death Us Do Part and Till Death….

902. Warren Mitchell

903. East End of London

904. Winston

905. Marigold

906. 47

907. Chas & Dave

908.	Rita
909.	1992
910.	West Ham United

WRITTEN BY – 2

911.	Roman's Empire	Harry Williams and Jack Williams
912.	The Rag Trade	Ronald Chesney and Ronald Wolfe
913.	Are You Being Served?	Jeremy Lloyd and David Croft
914.	Bottom	Adrian Edmondson and Rik Mayall
915.	Not On Your Nellie	Tom Brennand and Roy Bottomley
916.	Two Pints of Lager and a Packet of Crisps	Susan Nickson and Daniel Peak
917.	Till Death Us Do Part	Johnny Speight
918.	One Foot in the Grave	David Renwick
919.	Mind Your Language	Vince Powell
920.	Grace and Favour	Jeremy Lloyd and David Croft

MIND YOUR LANGUAGE

921.	Vince Powell
922.	42
923.	1977
924.	Jeremy Brown
925.	'The First Lesson'
926.	Uxbridge Technical College, Middlesex
927.	Ranjeet Singh

928.   Françoise Pascal

929.   Jamila Massey

930.   Miss Dolores Courtney

THREE UP, TWO DOWN

931.   The basement

932.   Rhonda

933.   1985

934.   Sam Tyler

935.   Michael Elphick, Angela Thorne, Lysette Anthony and
        Ray Burdis

936.   A taxidermist

937.   'Your Place oOr Mine?'

938.   Richard Ommanney

939.   Daphne Trenchard

940.   A photographer

YOU RANG, M'LORD?

941.   4

942.   Paul Shane

943.   1920s

944.   Bob Monkhouse

945.   Lord George Meldrum

946.   Cissy and Poppy

947.   Bill Pertwee

948.   Jimmy Perry and David Croft

949.   Norfolk (Lynford Hall, Lynford and Oxburgh Hall, Oxborough)

950.   1988

GALTON & SIMPSON

951.   1948

952.   Hancock's Half Hour

953.   OBEs

954.   Steptoe and Son

955.   Writers' Guild Award

956.   Casanova

957.   Steptoe and Son, and Steptoe and Son Ride Again

958.   Citizen James

959.   Alan (Galton) and Alan (Simpson)

960.   Alan Simpson, who was born 27 November 1929 (Ray Galton was born on 17 July 1930)

WATCHING

961.   7

962.   Paul Brown

963.   Emma Wray

964.   Merseyside

965.   Stoneway

966.   Perry Fenwick

967.   They watched customers and tried to guess their occupations, lifestyles and other facts about them

968.   ITV

969.   Birdwatching

970.   Brenda and Malcolm got married

BENIDORM

971.   Sheila Reid

972.   Derren Litten

973.   2007

974.   The Solana holiday resort

975.   Geoff Maltby

976.   Johnny Vegas

977. True

978. Hotel Sol Pelicanos-Ocas

979. Garvey

980. True

MAY TO DECEMBER

981. A PE teacher

982. Simone and Jamie

983. In Alex's office (she was a client)

984. London

985. Mrs Vera Flood and Hilary

986. 6

987. A solicitor

988. Anton Rodgers

989. Fleur

990. BBC1

LAST BROADCAST

991.	The Worker	1978
992.	Up Pompeii!	1970
993.	That's My Boy	1986
994.	Shelley	1992
995.	On the Buses	1973
996.	Is It Legal?	1998
997.	How Do You Want Me?	1999
998.	Brush Strokes	1991
999.	The Army Game	1961
1000.	Sensitive Skin	2007

NOTES:

NOTES:

NOTES:

NOTES:

NOTES:

NOTES:

NOTES:

www.apexpublishing.co.uk